Sing Around Scotland

Songs chosen by Morag Henriksen
and arranged by Barrie Carson Turner

illustrated by Harry Henriksen

Ward Lock Educational

First published 1985 by
Ward Lock Educational
47 Marylebone Lane
London W1M 6AX

A member of the Ling Kee Group
HONG KONG · TAIPEI · SINGAPORE · LONDON · NEW YORK

My thanks to everyone who helped me with this book but I dedicate it especially to Nancy Nicolson and Barrie Creed who revived my interest in folk-songs and encouraged me to sing again.

Morag Henriksen

Please note: Your local authority has a licence from the Performing Rights Society which covers the performance of musical works in schools. If you are using any of the songs in this book for a public performance, could you please send details to your Music Adviser. This will not involve you or your local authority in any extra payment. It will simply ensure that royalties are correctly allocated from the licence fee. Thank you.

Typeset by Gilbert Composing Services, Leighton Buzzard, Bedfordshire.
Printed by Mackays of Chatham Ltd.

Contents

Introduction

Highlands and Islands
Scotland   4
Leis an Lurgainn   6
The Christ child's lullaby   8
Brochan lom   10
The Dark Island   12
The Battle of the Braes   14
Air falalalo   16
Sound the pibroch   18
Faraway Tom   20

Glasgow
The welly boot song   22
Skyscraper wean   24
O'Hara's barra   26
The song of the Clyde   28
Johnny Lad   30
The red yo-yo   32
Hot Asphalt   34

Galloway
The Deil's awa' wi'th' exciseman   38
Coulter's candy   40
The Gallowa' hills   42
Ay waukin' o   44
Up in the morning early   46
The wee Kirkcudbright centipede   48

Orkney and Shetland
Chappin' at the door   52

Da rabbit's lullaby   54
Partans in his creel   56
Hame wi' de, Lowrie   58

Grampian
A pair o' nicky tams   60
The lum hat wantin' the croon   62
Men o' worth   63
Fareweel tae Tarwathie   66

Central Lowlands
The craw killed the pussy-o   68
Willie Lee   69
Henry Martin   72
The safari park song   74
Bonnie George Campbell   77
Jenny's bawbee   78
Katie Beardie   79
Four and twenty Hielandmen   80

Edinburgh
The sack 'em up boys   82
The fair lady   84
Waly waly   86

Borders
Riddles wisely expounded   88
The border widow's lament   89
Lock the door, Lariston   90

Glossary   92

Acknowledgements   93

Introduction

This collection attempts to represent each of the Scottish regions from Shetland to Stranraer and the Borders to the Butt of Lewis. It is impossible, of course; one book cannot do justice to the enormous variety of dialects and people that combine to make our mixter-maxter nation.

First and foremost, this is a book for use in schools and so I have chosen songs which appeal to children and are easy to sing. Songs that are well-worn in one region may be quite inscrutable to another, but the tunes bind all together. The Norse dialects of Shetland and Orkney, Hebridean Gaelic, Glasgow humour, couthy cornkisters and Border ballads, the songs of Robert Burns and the new songs of our industrial age all belong to Scotland and our heritage of song has influenced the music of the world.

Some of the longer ballads, like *The Battle of the Braes*, can be dramatised. Some are just wee snippets of nursery rhymes, but I have avoided singing games because their place is in the oral tradition of the playground—not pressed like wild flowers between the pages of a book. And I have avoided, above all, any songs that purvey thistles and tartan and Ma Granny's Hieland Hame—none of that kind of scunner!

An English translation of the Gaelic songs is provided so that the tunes are accessible to those unfamiliar with the language.

I have looked for songs everywhere: heard them over the phone, found them in books, tapes, the letter page of *The Scotsman* or taken them out of my head where they have been so long I cannot remember where I heard them. I have tried to spread the choice wide, historically as well as geographically, and to combine serious ballads with music-hall humour so that there is something for everyone.

Arranger's note

Sing Around Scotland includes folk-songs which have been sung from generation to generation and so passed down to us—often with many different variations of tune and words; some traditional songs with new words (and vice versa); and others which are entirely modern. Some songs may be recognisable as one-time television themes and quite a few are almost signature tunes of particular singers. All of them have completely new arrangements specially written for this book.

As all the tunes have been incorporated into the accompaniments, the musical arrangements will also serve as piano pieces in their own right. Chord symbols are provided for guitarists and to lead to further piano improvisations.

I transcribed the tunes of the songs from cassette recordings of Morag's unaccompanied singing. It is much quicker and easier to sing the songs than to try to track down printed copies of the music—but we also like to think that, by working in this way, we have carried on the tradition of passing on the songs through singing—even though the final result has been put into print.

Morag Henriksen

Barrie Carson Turner

2

Highlands and Islands

Scotland

Words: ALEXANDER GRAY

Tune: OLD GAELIC MELODY

1 This is my country,
   Land that begat me,
   These windy spaces
   Are surely my own.
   Those who here toil in
   The sweat of their faces,
   Are flesh of my flesh
   And bone of my bone.

2 Yet do your children
   Honour and love you,
   Harsh is your schooling
   But great is the gain.
   True hearts and strong limbs,
   The beauty of faces
   Kissed by the wind,
   And caressed by the rain.

The idea for this combination of words and tune came from the letters' page in **The Scotsman** *after Scotland's rugby team won the Triple Crown in 1984.*

   Bunessan is an old Gaelic hymn tune.

Leis an Lurgainn

Leis an Lurgainn o hi,
Leis an Lurgainn o ho
Beul an anamoich o hi,
'S fheudar falbh le 'cuid seol.

On the Lurgainn o hee
On the Lurgainn o ho
In the grey evening light
O'er the waves let us go.

1 An Cuan Eirinn o hi,
Muir ag eirigh o ho,
Cha bu leir dhiunn o hi,
Ni fo'n ghrein ach na neoil.
Leis an Lurgainn o hi, etc.

On the ocean o hee
Waves in motion o ho
Only clouds could we see
And the dark sea below.
On the Lurgainn o hee, etc.

2 Thuirt an sgiobair o hi,
Ri chuid ghillean o ho,
'Glacaibh misneach o hi
'S deanaibh dichoill, a sheoid.'
Leis an Lurgainn o hi, etc.

Skipper bellows, o hee,
To his fellows o ho
'Steady! Courage take ye
Though a tempest should blow.'
On the Lurgainn o hi, etc.

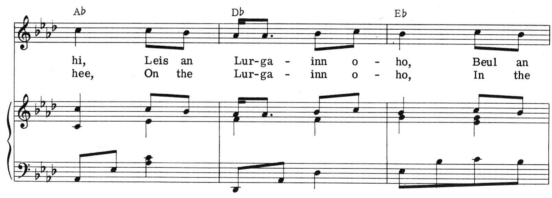

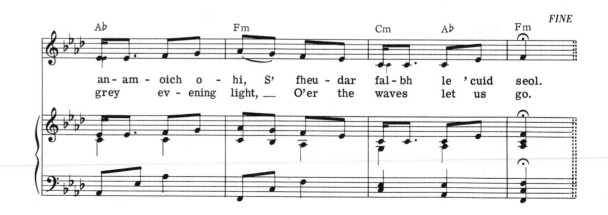

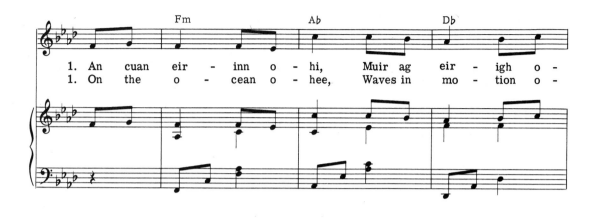

1. An cuan eir - inn o hi, Muir ag eir - igh o -
1. On the o - cean o - hee, Waves in mo - tion o -

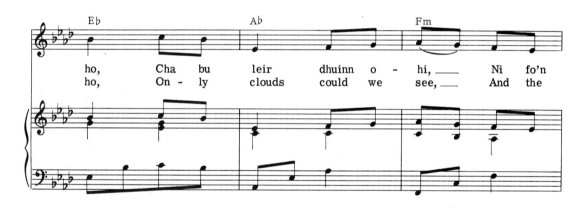

ho, Cha bu leir dhuinn o - hi, ____ Ni fo'n
ho, On - ly clouds could we see, ____ And the

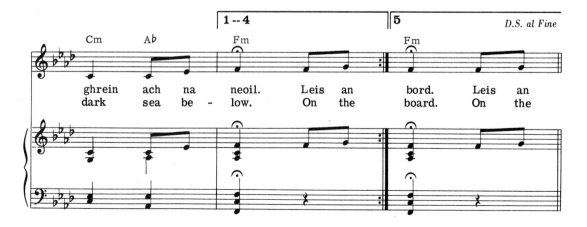

ghrein ach na neoil. Leis an bord. Leis an
dark sea be - low. On the board. On the

3 Suas a h-aodach o hi,
   Ri croinn chaola o ho
   Snamh cho actrom o hi,
   Ris an fhaolinn air lon.
   Leis an Lurgainn o hi, etc.

   'Crowd her sails on o hee,
   And though gales come o ho
   Like a seagull will she
   O'er the heaving waves go.'
   On the Lurgainn o hee, etc.

4 Muir 'ga bualadh o hi,
   Taobh an fhuaraidh o ho
   Bith'dh sinn buadhar o hi
   'S gillean uallach air bord
   Leis an Lurgainn o hi, etc.

   'Billows lashing o hee
   Waters crashing o ho.
   We're not flinching. You see
   There are stout lads on board.'
   On the Lurgainn o hee, etc.

Leis an Lurgainn is pronounced 'Laysh un Lorgeen'.

7

Taladh Chrisoda
(The Christ child's lullaby)

1 Mo ghaol, mo ghradh is m'eudal thu,
M'iunntas ur is m'eibhneas thu,
Mo mhacan alainn ceutach thu,
Chan fhiu mi-fhein bhith'd dhail.

Alleluia, alleluia,
Alleluia, alleluia.

My joy, my love, my darling thou,
My treasure new, my rapture thou,
My comely beauteous babeson thou,
Unworthy I to tend to thee.

2 Mo ghaol an t-suil a sheallas tlath,
Mo ghaol an cridh tha liont le gradh,
Ged is leanabh thu gun chail
Is lionmhor buaidh tha ort a fas.

Alleluia, alleluia, etc.

White son of hope and life art thou,
Of love the heart and eye art thou,
Though but a tender babe I bow
In heavenly rapture unto thee.

This is a very beautiful Christmas hymn from the Outer Isles.

8

thu, Chan fhiu mi fhèin bhith'd dhàil. _____
thou, Un - wor - thy I to tend to thee.

Al - le - lu - ia, Al - le - lu - ia, Al -

- le - lu - ia, Al - le - lu - ia. _____ My ia. _____

Brochan lom

Oh, brochan lom, tana lom, brochan lom
    sùghain,
Brochan lom, tana lom, brochan lom
    sùghain,
Brochan lom, tana lom, brochan lom
    sùghain,
Brochan lom, 's e tana lom, 's e brochan lom
    sùghain.

1 Brochan tana, tana, tana, brochan tana
    sùghain,
  Brochan tana, tana, tana, brochan tana
    sùghain,
  Brochan tana, tana, tana, brochan tana
    sùghain,
  Brochan lom, 's e tana lom, 's e brochan lom
    sùghain.

  Oh, brochan lom, etc.

2 Thugaibh aran do na balaich leis a'
    bhrochan sùghain,
  Thugaibh aran do na balaich leis a'
    bhrochan sùghain,
  Thugaibh aran do na balaich leis a'
    bhrochan sùghain,
  Brochan lom, 's e tana lom, 's e brochan lom
    sùghain.

  Oh, brochan lom, etc.

This is puirt a beul—*Gaelic mouth music for
dancing when people lacked a musician or
were too poor to own a fiddle. The words are
nonsense about watery porridge. Often they
were made up on the spur of the moment to
make people laugh. Try to make up your own
words.*

The Dark Island

Words: DAVID SILVER

Tune: TRADITIONAL

1 Away to the West's where I'm longing to be
Where the beauty of heaven unfolds by the sea,
Where the deep purple heather blooms fragrant
    and free
On a hilltop high above the Dark Island.

Oh, Isle of my childhood, I'm dreaming of thee
As the steamer leaves Oban and passes Tiree
Soon I'll capture the magic that lingers for me
When I'm back once more upon the Dark
    Island.

2 Oh, gentle the sea breeze that ripples the bay
Where the stream joins the ocean and young
    children play;
On the strand of pure silver I'll welcome each
    day
And I'll roam for evermore the Dark Island.

Oh, Isle of my childhood, etc.

The Dark Island is Barra in the Outer Hebrides. This
tune was the theme for a TV thriller in the sixties.

land. Oh, — isle of my child - hood I'm drea-ming of thee,

As the stea - mer leaves O - ban and pas - ses Ti - ree;

Soon I'll cap - ture the ma - gic that lin - gers for me, When I'm

back once more up - on the Dark — Is - land. 2. So land.

The Battle of the Braes

Words: 7:84 COMPANY

1 A Sheriff from the factor came
   And he came down our way,
   From Lord Macdonald he was sent
   To clear us out from Skye.

   Oh the battle was long but the people were
      strong
   You shoulda been there that day!
   (Repeat after each verse)

2 Oh had he come wi' fifty men
   He could not pass that day,
   For all the women from the Braes
   Went out to bar the way.

3 The Laird was angry; he was wild,
   Macdonald must not fail.
   He sent the Sheriff back again
   To throw us into jail.

4 And next came fifty policemen,
   From Glasgow they were sent,
   The Inverness police knew fine
   That what we said we meant.

5 A wet and dismal morning dawned
   As from Portree they rode,
   The men of Braes were up in time
   And met them on the road.

6 All day the cruel battle raged,
   We showed them we could fight.
   But five brave men were taken off
   To Inverness that night.

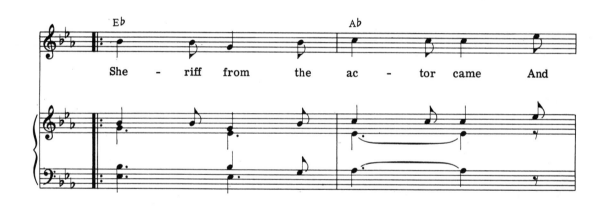

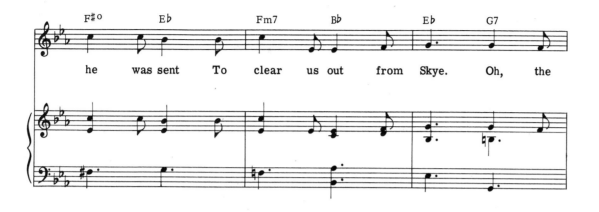

he was sent To clear us out from Skye. Oh, the

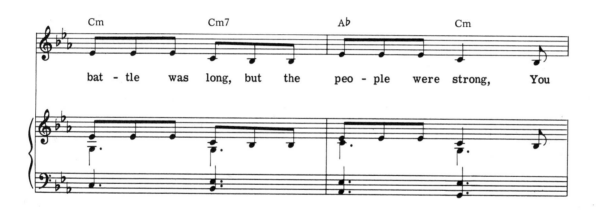

bat - tle was long, but the peo - ple were strong, You

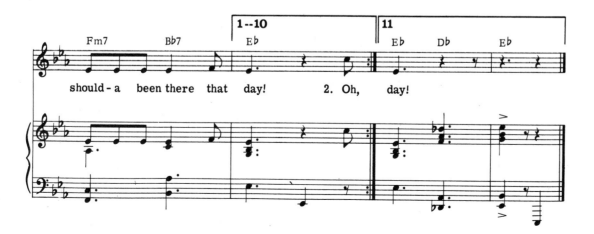

should - a been there that day! 2. Oh, day!

7   The Judge he found them guilty men
    And fined them two pounds ten,
    In half a minute it was paid
    And off they went again.

8   Once more Macdonald's anger broke.
    'Invade the Isle of Skye!
    Two thousand soldiers, boats and guns—
    The people must comply!'

9   'Oh, if we send one million men'
    In London they declared,
    'We'll never clear the Isle of Skye.
    The people are not scared.'

10   The police up in Inverness
    Demanded extra men,
    No other town in all the land
    Would help them out again.

11   So back the Sheriff came to Braes
    All Scotland watched them go.
    'Will you clear off Macdonald's land?'
    The people answered 'NO!'

After Culloden, the clan system began to break up. There were too many people for the land to support. Many had to leave. More were forcibly evicted to make way for big sheep farms or sporting estates.

Mostly the people did as they were told but, in 1882, the crofters in Braes of Portree on the Isle of Skye refused to pay their rent until they got back their common grazing land on Ben Lee.

The landlord, Lord Macdonald, tried to evict them but they burned the eviction notices and resisted arrest. The skirmish caught the attention of the Liberal press. Questions were asked in Parliament which led to a better security of tenure for crofters that has lasted to the present day.

Air falalalo

Words: HUGH ROBERTON

Tune: A MHAIRI BHAN OG

Air falalalo horo air falalalay,
Air falalalo horo air falalalay,
Air falalalo horo air falalalay,
Falee falo horo air falalalay.

1 There's lilt in the song I sing; there's laughter
    and love.
  There's tang o' the sea and blue from heaven
    above.
  Of reason there's none and why should there
    be forbye,
  With the fire in the blood and toes, the light in
    the eye.

Air falalalo, etc.

2 The heather's ablaze wi' bloom, the myrtle is
    sweet.
  There's song in the air; the road's a song at my
    feet.
  So step it along as light as the bird on the wing
  And stepping along let's join our voices and
    sing.

Air falalalo, etc.

3 And whether the blood be Highland, Lowland
    or no
  And whether the skin be white or black as the
    sloe,
  Of kith and of kin we're one, be it right, be it
    wrong
  If only our hearts beat true to the lilt of a song.

Air falalalo, etc.

love. _____ There's tang o' the sea and blue from hea-ven a-bove. _____ Of rea-son there's

none, and why_____ should there be for - bye, _____ With the fire in the

blood and toes, the light in the eye. _____ Air fal - al - al song. _____ Air fal - al - al

Sound the pibroch

1 Sound the pibroch loud and high
Frae John o' Groats to Isle of Skye,
Let a' the clans their slogans cry
And rise and follow Charlie.

Tha tighinn fodham, fodham, fodham,
Tha tighinn fodham, fodham, fodham,
Tha tighinn fodham, fodham, fodham,
Tha tighin fodham eirigh!*

2 See a small devoted band
By dark Loch Shiel has ta'en its stand,
They proudly vow wi' heart and hand
To die for royal Charlie.

Tha tighinn fodham, etc.

3 On dark Culloden's field of gore
'Hark, hark', they shout, 'Claymore!
    'Claymore!'
They bravely fight—what can they more?
They die for royal Charlie.

Tha tighinn fodham, etc.

No more we'll see such deeds again
Deserted is each Highland glen,
And lonely cairns are o'er the men
Who fought and died for Charlie.

18

Chorus translation

I must rise and follow, follow
I must rise and follow, follow,
I must rise and follow on.
Rise and follow Charlie.

*Ha cheen foh-um ay-ree

In 1745 Prince Charles Edward Stuart landed in Moidart with a few followers. He raised his standard at Glenfinnan on the shores of Loch Shiel and the clans gathered till he had a great army of Highlanders intent on winning back the throne for his father, James, who was an exile in France.

The Jacobite army reached Derby. There was panic in London and, had they carried on, Prince Charlie would probably have won his cause but he was ill-advised. The army lost heart so far from home. They turned back and were heavily defeated at Culloden outside Inverness. Prince Charlie became a fugitive with a price on his head, the subject of many romantic songs. The Highlanders were persecuted, slaughtered or forced into exile. The House of Hanover was secure and the Highland Clearances had begun.

*   If preferred, the Gaelic *or* the English chorus may be sung throughout.

19

Faraway Tom

DAVE GOULDER

1 When the calendar brings in the cuckoo
   And the summer comes following on,
   And the thin mists of day see him running away;
   Then they know him as Faraway Tom.

2 The earth is his bed and his pillow
   And the sheets are the clothes he has on.
   He spends all afternoon, hunting the moon,
   Till it rises for Faraway Tom.

3 He sees the fox leaving its hollow,
   And he knows where the badger is gone.
   He watches the fawn in the sheltering thorn,
   But they don't see old Faraway Tom.

4 He knows nothing of letters or learning
   And of manners and such he has none.
   He numbers the seasons on fingers and toes
   As they pass over Faraway Tom.

5 But what of the winters to follow
   When age and cold winds bring him down?
   Where will he lie when the snow fills the sky
   And the years tell on Faraway Tom?

Glasgow

The welly boot song

Words: GEORGE McEWAN

If it wisnae fir yer wellies where wid ye be?
You'd be in the hospital or infirmary,
For you wid ha'e a dose o' the flu or even
*   pleurisy*
If you didnae ha'e your feet in your wellies.

1 Oh, wellies they are wonderful. Oh, wellies they
        are swell.
   For they keep oot the watter and they keep in
        the smell
   And when you're sitting in a room you can
        always tell
   When somebody takes aff his wellies.

   If it wisnae, etc.

2 And when you're oot walkin' in the country wi'
        a bird
   And you're strolling over fields just like a
        farmer's herd
   When someone shouts, 'Keep off the grass!'
        and you think, 'How absurd!'
   Then SQUELCH! You find why farmers a'
        wear wellies.

   If it wisnae, etc.

3 There's fishermen and firemen, there's farmers
        an' a'
   Men oot diggin' ditches and workin' in the
        snaw.
   This country it wid grind tae a halt and no' a
        thing wid graw
   If it wisnae for the workers in their wellies.

   If it wisnae, etc.

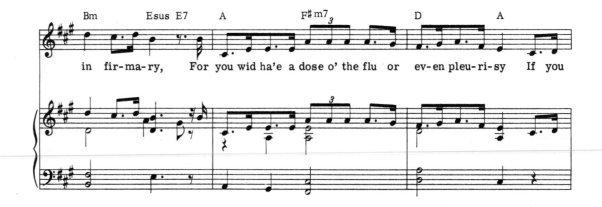

Skyscraper wean

ADAM MACNAUGHTON

1 I'm a skyscraper wean; I live on the nineteenth
      flair,
   An' I'm no gaun oot tae play ony mair,
   'Cause since we moved tae Castlemilk I'm
      wasting away
   'Cause I get one less meal every day.

   Oh, ye cannae fling pieces oot a twenty storey
      flat.
   Seven hundred hungry weans 'll testify tae that.
   If it's butter, cheese or jeely, if the breid is plain
      or pan,
   The odds against it reaching earth are ninety-
      nine tae wan.

2 On the first day ma maw flung oot a daud o'
      Hovis broon;
   It came skytin' oot the windae and went up
      instead o' doon.
   Noo every twenty-seven hoors it comes back
      intae sight
   'Cause my piece went intae orbit and became a
      satellite.

   Oh, ye cannae, etc.

3 On the second day ma maw flung me oot a piece
      again
   It went an' hit the pilot of a fast low-flying
      plane.
   He scraped it aff his goggles, shouting through
      the intercom,
   'The Clydeside Reds have got me wi' a breid an'
      jeely bomb!'

   Oh, ye cannae, etc.

24

4 On the third day ma maw thought she'd try
  another throw;
  The Salvation Army band was standin' doon
  below.
  'Onward, Christian Soldiers' was the piece they
  should have played
  But the oompah man was playing ma piece
  and marmalade.

  Oh, ye cannae, etc.

5 So we've wrote away tae Oxfam tae try an' get
  some aid
  An' a' the weans in Castlemilk have formed a
  piece brigade;
  We're gonnae march on George's Square
  demanding civil rights
  Like nae mair hooses ower piece-flingin'
  heights

  Oh, ye cannae, etc.

*When the slums were demolished the people were
housed in tower blocks on the outskirts of Glasgow.
This nostalgic 'protest song' remembers the good old
days when mothers could make sandwiches or jeelie
pieces, put them in a paper bag and throw them out
the window to their children playing in the street
outside.*

  Crisps and sweets were luxuries in those days.

O'Hara's barra

Words: JIMMIE MACGREGOR

Tune: TRADITIONAL

1. As I came in by Glesca toon,
I met wi' wee O'Hara;
I gied him a lick o' ma candy stick,
And he gied me a hurl in his barra.
Noo the bonnie wee barra's mine,
It disnae belang tae wee O'Hara,
For the fly wee Jock, he stuck tae ma rock
So by jings, I'm stickin' tae his barra.

2. As I came in by Glesca toon,
I met wi' wee McCleary;
I gied him a plunk o' ma jorrie bool,
And he gied me a birl o' his peerie.
Noo the bonnie wee peerie's mine,
It disnae belang tae wee McCleary;
He's nae fool, for he stuck tae ma bool,
So by jings, I'm stickin tae his peerie.

3. As I came in by Glesca toon,
I met wi' Jimmy Logie;
I gied him a keek at ma gird and cleek,
And he gied me a bash at his bogie.
Noo the bonnie wee bogie's mine,
It disnae belang tae Jimmy Logie;
Fur the cheeky wee sneak, he stuck tae ma cleek,
So by jings, I'm stickin' tae his bogie.

This traditional street song has had two more verses added by Jimmie MacGregor to commemorate old street games.

A jorrie bool is a glass marble. A peerie is a spinning-top. A gird and a cleek is a hoop and a stick for bowling along the road. 'A bash at his bogie' means a try-out of his homemade cart probably made of some pram wheels and a box.

26

Noo the bon-nie wee bar-ra's mine, It dis-nae be-long tae wee O'

Ha - ra, For the fly wee Jock, he stuck tae ma rock, So by

jings, I'm stick-in' tae his bar - ra. 2. As bo - gie.

The song of the Clyde

1 I'll sing of a river I'm happy beside
  And the song that I sing is the song of the Clyde
  Of all Scottish rivers it's dearest tae me;
  It flows from Leadhills all the way to the sea.
  It borders the orchards of Lanark so fair,
  Meanders through meadows with sheep grazing
      there,
  But from Glasgow to Greenock in towns on
      each side—
  The hammers' ding-dong is the song of the
      Clyde.

  Oh, the river Clyde, the wonderful Clyde!
  The name of it thrills me and fills me with
      pride,
  And I'm satisfied whate'er may betide;
  The sweetest of songs is the song of the Clyde.

2 Imagine you've left Craigendoran behind
  And windhappy yachts by Kilcreggan you'll
      find.
  In Kirn and Dunoon and Inellan you'll stay
  And Scotland's Madeira that's Rothesay they
      say.
  Or maybe by Fairlie and Largs you will go
  Or over to Millport that thrills people so,
  Maybe journey to Arran—it can't be denied
  Those scenes all belong to the song of the
      Clyde

  Oh, the river Clyde, etc.

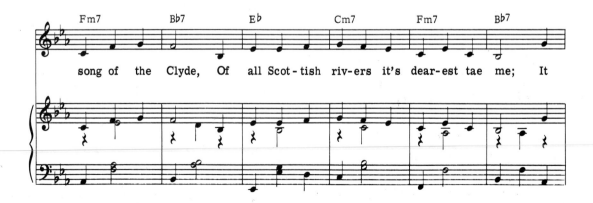

28

flows from Lead-hills all the way to the sea. It bor-ders the or-chards of

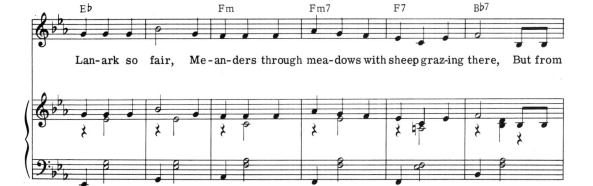

Lan-ark so fair, Me-an-ders through mea-dows with sheep graz-ing there, But from

Glas-gow to Green-ock in towns on each side— The ham-mer's ding-dong is the

3   There's Paw an' Maw on Glasgow Broomielaw
They're goin' Doon The Watter fur The Fair.
There's Bob an' Mary on the Govan Ferry
Wishin' jet propulsion would be there.
There's steamers cruisin' and there's bodies
       snoozin'
And there's laddies fishin' frae the pier,
and Paw's perspirin', very near expirin'
As he rows a boat frae there tae here.
Wi' eyes a-flashin, it is voted smashin'
Tae be walkin' daily on the Prom.
And May and Evelyn are in seventh heaven
As they stroll along wi' Dick an' Tom,
And Dumbarton Rock tae every Jean and Jock
Extends a welcome that is high and wide,
Seems to know that they are on their homeward
       way
To hear the song of the Clyde.

Oh, the river Clyde, etc.

(The last verse is a 'patter' verse to be sung at twice
the normal speed.)

*This trip down the Clyde is a period piece now. The
shipyards are mostly silent and Glasgow's holiday-
makers fly to Majorca and Tenerife rather than sail
to resorts 'Doon the watter'.*

Music continued overleaf

Music for **The Song of the Clyde** *(continued)*

song of the Clyde. Oh, the riv - er Clyde, the won-der-ful Clyde! The

name of it thrills me and fills me with pride, And I'm sat - is - fied what-

e'er may be-tide; The sweet-est of songs is the song of the Clyde. 2.Im- Clyde.

Johnny Lad

1 I bought a wife in Edinburgh for a bawbee.
   I got a farthing back again tae buy tobacco
   wi'.

   And wi' you and wi' you and wi' you
   Johnny Lad.
   I'll dance the buckles off my shoon
   Wi' you, my Johnny Lad.

2 As I was walking early I chanced to see the
   Queen,
   She was playing at the fitba' wi' the lads in
   Glasgow Green.

   And wi' you and wi' you, etc.

3 The captain o' the ither side was scoring wi'
   great style,
   So the Queen she cried a polisman and she
   clapped him in the jyle.

   And wi' you and wi' you, etc.

4 Noo Samson was a michty man. He focht wi'
   cuddies' jaws
   And he won a score o' battles wearing
   crimson flannel drawers.

   And wi' you and wi' you, etc.

5   There was a man o' Nineveh and he was
       wondrous wise.
    He louped intae a bramble bush and
       scratched oot baith his eyes.

And wi' you and wi' you, etc.

6   And when he saw his eyes wis oot he wis gey
       troubled then
    So he louped intae anither bush and
       scratched them in again.

And wi' you and wi' you, etc.

7.   Noo Johnny is a bonny lad, he is a lad o'
       mine.
    I've never had a better lad and I've had
       twenty-nine.

And wi' you and wi' you, etc.

The red yo-yo

MATT McGINN

1 Wee Ann had a yo-yo
To school she did go, though
She shouldnae hae ta'en it at a',
It fell frae her hand and it rolled on the ground
And it went through a hole in the wa'.

Did you find a red yo-yo
Red yo-yo, red yo-yo?
Did you find a red yo-yo
With a wee yellow string?

2 Now the daring wee Annie
She went tae the jannie,
A dacent wee man as a rule,
And it's pleasing tae tell that he rang on his bell
And he asked a' the weans in the school . . .

Did you find, etc.

3 The police were concerned
When the story they learned
And they left a' their murders aside,
The whole of the Force was alerted—of course—
And they went on the telly and cried . . .

Did you find, etc.

4 From Peking to Paris
And a' roond The Barras
The people they searched high and low,
Till finally Annie announced that her Granny
Had bought her another yo-yo.

And it was a red yo-yo,
Red yo-yo, red yo-yo,
And it was a red yo-yo
With a wee yellow string.

The Barras is a street market in Glasgow.

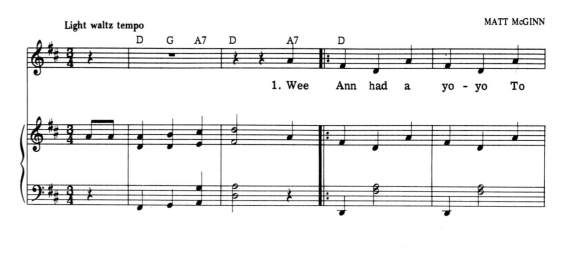

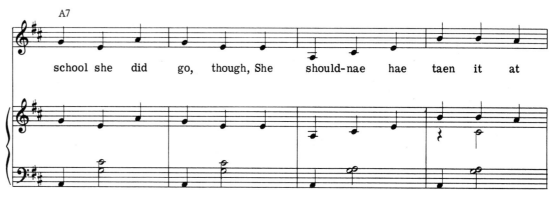

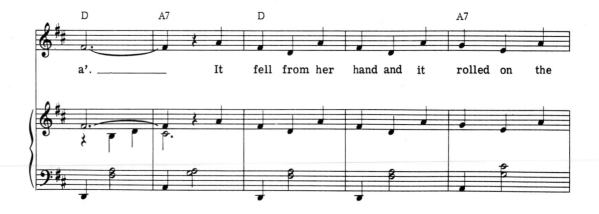

32

ground And it went through a hole in the wa'. _____ Did you

find a red yo - yo, Red yo - yo, red yo - yo? Did you

1--4 D A7 **5** D

find a red yo - yo With a wee yel - low string? 2. Now the string?

Hot Asphalt

1 Well, good evening to you, jolly lads,
I'm glad to see you well.
If you'll gather all around me, boys,
This story I will tell.
I've got a situation and begorrah and begob
I can say that I've a weekly wage of nineteen
    bob.
It's twelve months last October
Since I left my native home
After working in Killarney, boys,
To cut the harvest down.
But now I wear a gansey and around my waist a
    belt—
I'm the gaffer o' the lads that lay
The Hot Asphalt.

We laid it in the hollow and we laid it in the flat
And if it doesn't last forever then I'll surely eat
    my hat,
For now I wear a gansey and around my waist a
    belt—
I'm the gaffer o' the lads that lay The Hot
    Asphalt.

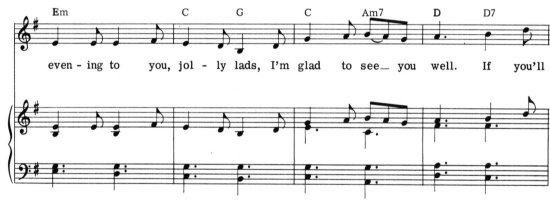

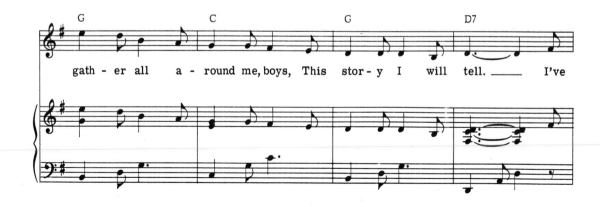

2 Well, the other day a policeman comes
   And he says to me, 'McGuire,
   Would you kindly let me light my pipe
   Down at your boiler fire?'
   And then he stands before it
   With his coat tails up so neat.
   'Here,' says I, 'Me dacent man, you'd better
   Go and mind your beat.'
   'Ah well', says he, 'I'm down on you
   I'm up to all your pranks
   Sure, I take you for a traitor
   From the Tipperary Banks.'
   Then I hit him from the shoulder,
   And I gave him such a welt
   That he landed in the boiler
   Full of Hot Asphalt.

   We laid it in the hollow, etc.

3 Well, we pulled him out and dried him
   And we put him in a tub
   And with warm and soapy water
   We began to rub and scrub,
   Ah but never the divil the tar came off
   It turned as hard as stone,
   And with every scrub we gave him
   You could hear that copper groan.
   'Twixt the rubbing and the scrubbing
   Sure he caught his death of cold,
   And for scientific purposes
   His body it was sold.
   In the Kelvingrove Museum, sure,
   He's hanging by his belt
   As a monument to the Irish
   Laying Hot Asphalt.

   We laid it in the hollow, etc.

The first Irish to come to Scotland gave their name and their language to the country. They were the Scots. In the following centuries many people crossed the Irish Sea one way or another in search of livelihood.

In the 19th century the canals and roads and heavy industry of Scotland's Industrial Revolution depended on gangs of Irish navvies. Glasgow still has a large Irish population with their own football team.

'Hot Asphalt' (pronounced 'Hot Ashfelt') is a music-hall song.

Galloway

The Deil's awa' wi' th' exciseman

ROBERT BURNS

1 The Deil cam fiddlin' through the toun
And danced awa' wi' th' exciseman,
And ilka wife cried, 'Auld Mahoun,
I wish you luck o' the prize, man.'

The Deil's awa,' the Deil's awa',
The Deil's awa' wi' th' exciseman.
He's danced awa', he's danced awa',
He's danced awa' wi' th' exciseman.

2 We'll mak oor malt. We'll brew our drink.
We'll dance and sing and rejoice, man,
And mony braw thanks to the muckle black
    Deil
That danced awa' wi' th' exciseman.

The Deil's awa', etc.

3 There's threesome reels; there's foursome
    reels
There's hornpipes and strathspeys, man,
But the ae best dance that cam o'er our land
Was 'The Deil's Awa' Wi' Th' Exciseman'.

The Deil's awa', etc.

Robert Burns worked as an exciseman, a Customs
officer, in Dumfries during the last few years of his
life. The excisemen were as much of a joke then as
income-tax men are today. There was a great deal of
smuggling in the Solway area to avoid Government
tax on brandy, lace, tobacco and tea and people all
over Scotland made their own whisky and beer in
secret to dodge the Customs and Excisemen.

Coulter's candy

Ally bally ally bally bee,
Sittin' on yer mammy's knee,
Greetin' for anither bawbee
Tae buy mair Coulter's candy.

1   Ally bally ally bally bee,
   When you grow up you'll go to sea,
   Makin' pennies for your daddy and me,
   Tae buy mair Coulter's candy.

   Ally bally, etc.

2   Mammy gie me ma thrifty doon,
   Here's auld Coulter comin' roon,
   Wi' a basket on his croon,
   Selling Coulter's candy

   Ally bally, etc.

3   Little Annie's greetin' tae,
   Sae whit can puir wee Mammy dae,
   But gie them a penny atween them twae,
   Tae buy mair Coulter's candy.

   Ally bally, etc.

4   Puir wee Jeannie, she wis lookin' awfy thin,
   A rickle o 'banes covered ower wi' skin,
   Noo she's gettin' a wee double chin,
   Wi' sookin' Coulter's candy.

   Ally bally, etc.

40

1,2,3 **4** *D.S. al Fine*

Robert Coltart (Coulter) was a familiar and popular figure in the towns of Dumfries-shire. He travelled around selling his homemade sweeties and singing the chorus of the song in the same way as an ice-cream van nowadays plays a tune to attract children's attention.

The Gallowa' hills

1 Oh, I'll tak my plaidie contented tae be,
A wee bittie kilted abune my knee,
An' I'll gie my pipes anither blaw
An' I'll gang oot ower the hills tae Gallowa'.

Oh, the Gallowa' hills are covered wi' broom,
Wi' heather bells in bonny bloom,
Wi' heather bells an' rivers a'
An' I'll gang oot ower the hills tae Gallowa'.

2 For I say bonnie lassie it's will ye come wi'
me
Tae share your lot in a strange country
For tae share your lot when doon fa's a'
An' I'll gang oot ower the hills tae Gallowa'.

Oh, the Gallowa' hills, etc.

3 For I'll sell my rock. I'll sell my reel.
I'll sell my granny's spinning-wheel.
I will sell them a' when doon fa's a'
An' I'll gang oot ower the hills tae Gallowa'.

Oh, the Gallowa' hills, etc.

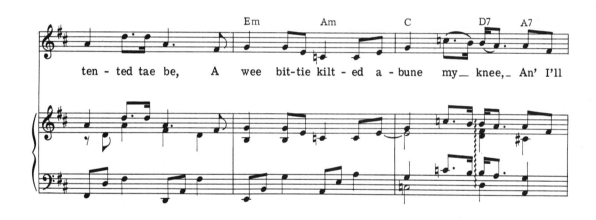

William Nicolson was a wandering minstrel who lived and roamed and sang his ballads round Galloway from 1793 to 1849. His song, The Braes of Galloway has changed through the years and this version is from the singing of Jeannie Robertson, herself a legendary ballad-singer.

42

Ay waukin' o

ROBERT BURNS

Ay waukin' o
Waukin' ay and wearie,
Sleep I can get nane
For thinkin' o' ma dearie
Ay waukin' o.

1 Spring's a pleasant time
   Flowers o' every colour.
   The water rins ower the heugh
   And I long for my lover.

   Ay waukin' o, etc.

2 When I sleep I dream.
   When I wauk I'm eerie.
   Sleep I can get nane
   For thinkin' o' ma dearie.

   Ay waukin' o, etc.

3 Lonely night comes on.
   A' the lave are sleepin'.
   I think on my braw lad
   And I blear my e'en wi' greetin'.

   Ay waukin' o, etc.

44

1. Spring's a plea - sant time, Flowers o' ev - ery col - our. The wa-ter rins ower the heugh, And I long for my lov - er. gree - tin'. o.

Up in the morning early

ROBERT BURNS

Up in the morning's no for me,
Up in the morning early!
When a' the hills are covered wi' snaw
I'm sure it's winter fairly!

1 Cauld blaws the wind frae east to west,
  The drift is driving sairly,
  Sae loud and shrill's I hear the blast—
  I'm sure it's winter fairly!

  Up in the morning's, etc.

2 The birds sit chittering in the thorn,
  A' day they fare but sparely;
  And lang's the night frae e'en to morn—
  I'm sure it's winter fairly

  Up in the morning's, etc.

Brightly

1. Cauld blows the wind frae east __ to west, The drift __ is driv - ing sair - ly, Sae loud and shrill's I hear __ the blast— I'm sure __ it's win - ter fair - ly!

Burns tried unsuccessfully to be a farmer so he knew
all about the miseries of having to get up very early
on a cold, dark winter's morning.

46

Up in the mor - ning's no __ for me, Up in the mor - ning

ear - ly! When a' the hills are cov - ered wi' snaw I'm __

sure __ it's win - ter fair - ly! 2. The fair - ly!

The wee Kirkcudbright centipede

MATT McGINN

1 The wee Kirkcudbright centipede, she was
very sweet,
She was ever so proud of every one of her
hundred feet.
Early every morning her neighbours came to
glance.
She always entertained them with a beautiful
little dance.

*Her leg at number ninety-four gave ninety-five
a shunt.*
*Legs numbers one and two were twistin' out in
front.*
*As legs numbers nine and ten were wrigglin' up
the side*
*Legs seventy-three and four were doing the
Palais Glide.*

2 Neighbour Jenny Longlegs with jealousy was
mad.
She went out and bought herself a pencil and a
pad.
She came a month of mornings and made a
careful note
Of every step the centipede took and this is
what she wrote.

Her leg, etc.

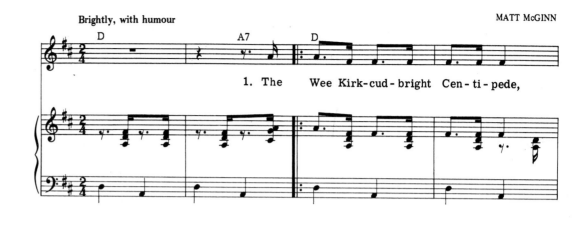

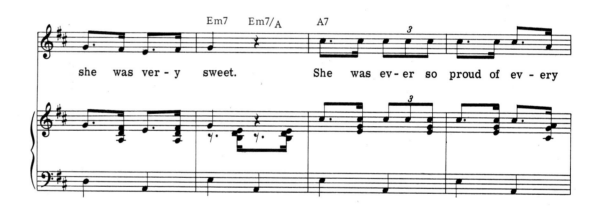

48

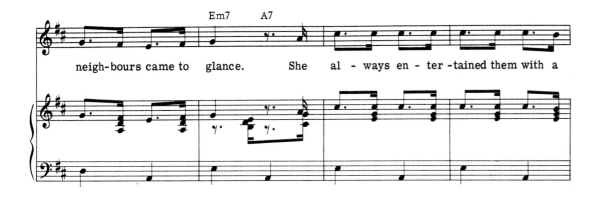

neigh-bours came to glance. She al-ways en-ter-tained them with a

beau-ti-ful lit-tle dance. Her leg at num-ber nine-ty-four gave

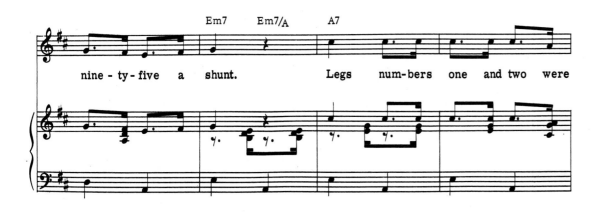

nine-ty-five a shunt. Legs num-bers one and two were

3 Armed with exact notation, young
   Jenny Longlegs tried
To dance just like the centipede. She failed and
   nearly cried.
She grabbed hold of the centipede. She says,
   'Now have a look
And tell me how you do the steps I've written in
   my book.'

Her leg, etc.

4 Said the centipede, 'Do I do that?' She tried to
   demonstrate.
She'd never thought on the thing before, she got
   in a terrible state.
Her hundred legs were twisted, she got tied up
   in a fankle.
She fractured seven shinbones, fourteen
   kneecaps and an ankle.

Her leg, etc.

5 As legs numbers one and two were tied to three
   and four,
Legs numbers five and six were trampled on the
   floor.
Leg number fifteen was attacked by number
   ten.
Ninety-seven and ninety-eight will never dance
   again.

*The wee Kirkcudbright centipede she suffered
   terrible pain
And some of us were very surprised she ever
   danced again.
But now she tells her neighbours, everyone that
   calls to see:
'Never try an explanation of what comes
   naturally'.*

49

Kirkcudbright (pronounced Kirkoobree) is a town in Galloway but the song has no real connection with it. Matt McGinn just liked the sound of the words.

twist - in' out in front. As legs num-bers nine and ten were

wrig - glin' up the side. Legs sev-en-ty - three and four were

do - ing the Pal - ais Glide. ly.

Orkney and Shetland

Chappin' at the door

1 Why, there's somebody chappin' at the door,
　　Jock Scott,
Why, a-chap-chap-chappin' at the door!
It's a cauld dark night and we dinnae hae a light
An' there isna any rug tae the floor.
Oh, I sleep at the back o' the bed, Jock Scott,
While thoo're aye gey weel to the fore
So I'll lave it tae thee tae get oot o' bed an' see
Wha's a-chap-chap-chappin' at the door.
At the door, at the door,
Aye, a-chap-chap-chappin' at the door.
So I'll lave it tae thee tae get oot o' bed an' see
Wha's a-chap-chap-chappin' at the door.

2 Na, there's naebody chappin' at the door,
　　Jean Scott,
No a-chap-chap-chappin' at the door.
It's the wind in the sneck or we maybe hae a
　　leck
An' she's drippin' wi' a pleenk on the floor.
So I'll bide whaur I am in me bed, Jean Scott,
An' we'll baith hae a right good snore,
For the man isna right wha'd be oot on sic a
　　night
Tae come chap-chap-chappin' at the door.
At the door, at the door,
Aye, a chap-chap-chappin' at the door.
For the man isna right wha'd be oot on sic a
　　night
Tae come chap-chap-chappin' at the door.

52

Da rabbit's lullaby

Words: LARRY PETERSON

Tune: VAGALAND

Hushie-baa, Fluffy,
Hushie-baa-baa.
Du's da best rabbit
At ever I saa.

1   Da nicht is dat caald;
    Du sanna gen furt.
    Come here an A'll tak
    Dee up i my skurt.

Hushie-baa, Fluffy, etc.

2   I kyin at du laeks
    Da aald taatit-rug,
    An dere du sall lie
    Sae warm an sae snug.

Hushie-baa, Fluffy, etc.

3   Da kye an da hens
    Is aa ida byre,
    An du sall sleep here
    At da side o da fire.

Hushie-baa, Fluffy, etc.

4   Sae close du dy een,
    An faa du asleep,
    Da moarn du sall get
    A piece o a neep.

Hushie-baa, Fluffy, etc.

54

Partans in his creel

1 Oh I lay in bed ower lang this morning
Heedless o' me mither's warning,
Turned and twisted all night long
And never closed an e'e.
While outside a million stars were winkin',
Sleep it widna come for thinkin',
Thinkin' o' the lovin' words
That Willy said tae me.
Oh, Willy's tall and Willy's bonny
Willy has na muckle money,
No that siller matters
When I ken I lo'e him weel.

So I think I'd better tarry,
Bide a wee afore I marry,
Bide till Willy's catchin'
Mair than partans in his creel.

2 For me mither calls me young and silly,
Far too young tae marry Willy,
Seventeen come Christmas Day
To Willy's twenty-three.
And for a' he's ever saved a shilling
'T widna gie a cat a living,
A' the work that Willy does
Is running efter me.
Oh, Willy's slow and Willy's lazy
Willy taks things ower easy,
Faither says he's nothing but
A trowie ne'er-do-weel.

So I think, etc.

56

3 There's a peady croft amang the heather
Whaur he says we'll bide together,
There he'll mak' a living
Wi' his boatie on the sea.
There's a wee bit hoose his faither biggit,
Stootly perched and snugly riggit,
Waitin' tae be taken ower
By Willie and by me.
But Willie stands aboot and whistles
Willie's fields are fu' o' thistles,
Thistles never brought a body
Ony milk or meal.

So I think, etc.

Hame wi' de, Lowrie

Hame wi' de, hame wi' de, Lowrie,
Tae rin efter me du's no blate,
For I want a lad daet is bonny
No een wi' a face like a skate.

Grampian

A pair o' nicky tams

Tune: QUEER FOLK I' THE SHAWS

1 Fan I was only ten years auld I left the pairish schweel.
   My faither fee'd me tae The Mains tae chaw his milk and meal,
   First I pit on my narrow breeks tae hap my spinnel trams,
   Syne buckled aroon my knappin' knees a pair o' nicky tams.

2 First I gaed on for Baillie loon and syne gaed on for third
   And syne of course I had tae get the horseman's grip an' word,
   A loaf o' breid tae be my piece an' a bottle for drinkin' drams,
   Ye couldnae gang through the calf house door without your nicky tams.

3 The fairmer I am wi' eynoo he's wealthy but he's mean.
   Though corn is cheap his horse is poor, his harness fairly deen.
   He gars us load our carts ower fou, his conscience has nae qualms,
   Fan breist straps break there's naethin' like a pair o' nicky tams.

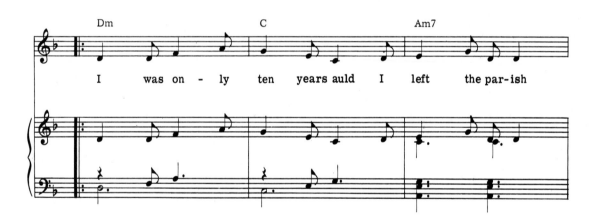

60

chaw his milk and meal. _____ First I pit on my

nar-row breeks tae hap my spin-nel trams, _____ Syne buck-led a - roon my

knap - pin knees a pair o' nick-y tams. _____ 2. First tams. _____

4 I'm courtin' bonnie Annie noo, Rob Tamson's
      kitchie deem,
  She is five and forty and I am seventeen.
  She clorts a muckle piece tae me wi' different
      kinds o' jams
  And tells me ilka night how she admires my
      nicky tams.

5 I startit oot ae Sunday morn the kirkie for tae
      gang,
  My collar it was unco tight, my breeks were
      nane ower lang.
  I had my Bible in my pooch, likewise my book
      o' Psalms,
  When Annie roared, 'Ye muckle gowk! Tak off
      your nicky tams!'

6 Though unco sweer, I took them off, the lassie
      for tae please
  And syne of course, my breeks they lirkit up
      aroon' my knees,
  A wasp gaed crawlin' up my leg in the middle o'
      the psalms
  Oh never again will I ride tae kirk wi' oot my
      nicky tams!

*The unmarried farmhands lived in a bothy and
amused themselves by sitting on the cornkist, the big
grain bin, and singing bothy ballads or cornkisters',
often funny, sometimes bawdy, frequently telling of
the bad working conditions in one farm or another.
    Nicky tams were the leather thongs a farmhand
tied round his trouser-legs to stop them flapping.*

The lum hat wantin' the croon

1. The burn was big wi' spate
   An' there cam tumblin' doon
   Tapsalteerie the half o' a gate,
   An auld fish hake an' a great muckle skate
   An' a lum hat wantin' the croon.

2. An auld wife stood on the bank
   As they gied soomin' roon.
   She took a guid look an' then quo' she
   'There's food an' there's firin' gaun doon
      tae the sea
   An' a lum hat wantin' the croon.'

3. So she grippit the branch o' a saugh,
   She kickit aff ane o' her shoon.
   She stuck oot her foot, but it caught in the
      gate
   An' awa she went wi' the great muckle skate
   An' the lum hat wantin' the croon.

4. A fisher was walkin' the deck,
   By the light o' his pipe an' the moon,
   When he saw an auld body astride o' a gate,
   Come bobbin' along on the waves wi' a skate
   An' a lum hat wantin' the croon.

5. 'There's a man overboard,' said he.
   'Ye leear,' quo' she, 'Sure, i'll droon.
   A man on a board? It's a wife on a gate.
   It's auld Mistress Mackintosh here wi' a
      skate
   An' a lum hat wantin' the croon.'

6 Was she nippit to death at the Pole?
   Has India bakit her broon?
   I canna tell that, but whatever her fate
   I'll bet that ye'll find it was shared by a gate
   An' a lum hat wantin' the croon.

7 There's a moral attached tae my song,
   On greed ye should aye gie a froon,
   When ye think o' the wife that was lost for the gate,
   The auld fish hake and the great muckle skate
   And the lum hat wantin' the croon.

ARCHIE FISHER

Slow and quietly flowing

Men o' worth

1 Leave the land behind, laddie, better days to
      find.
   The companies have the money and will soon
      teach you the skill.
   Green fields far away, laddie, The Forties and
      The Brae,
   Be a mudman or a roustabout, you'll soon learn
      how to drill.
   But who will tend the sheep when I'm far o'er
      the deep
   On the Neptune or the Sea Quest when the snow
      comes to the hill?

   Flotta to Kishorn a new industry is born,
   And Peterhead and Cromarty will never be the
      same.

Continued overleaf

Men o' worth *continued*

2 Leave the fishing trade, lad, there's
    money to be made
The handline and the Shetland yawl
    are from a bygone day.
Come tae Aiberdeen, laddie, sights
    ye've never seen.
Be a welder on the pipe-line or a fitter
    at Nigg Bay.
But when the job is o'er and my boat
    rots on the shore
How will I feed my family when the
    companies move away?

Flotta to Kishorn, etc.

3 There's harbours to be built, lad,
    there's rigs tae tow and tilt
To stand upon the ocean bed like
    pylons in the sea.
Pipe-lines to be laid and a hundred
    different trades,
That will earn a decent living wage
    for the likes of you and me.
I ken you're men o' worth, you're the
    best that's in the North.
No men o' greed but men who need
    the work that's come your way.

Flotta to Kishorn, etc.

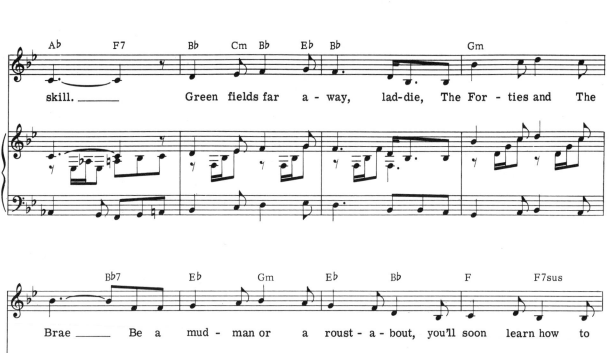

skill. ____ Green fields far a - way, lad-die, The For - ties and The

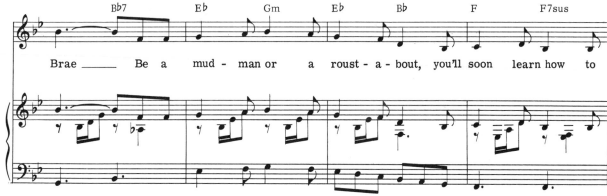

Brae ____ Be a mud - man or a roust-a-bout, you'll soon learn how to

drill. ____ But who will tend the sheep ____ when I'm far o'er the

deep On the Nep - tune or the Sea Quest when the snow comes to the hill? ___

Flot - ta to Kish - orn a new in - dus - try is born, ___ And

Pet - er-head and Cro - mar-ty will nev-er be the same. ___ same. ___

Fareweel tae Tarwathie

1 Fareweel tae Tarwathie, adieu, Mormond Hill,
And the dear land o' Crimond, I bid you
    fareweel.
I am bound now for Greenland and ready to
    sail,
In hopes to find riches a-hunting the whale.

2 Our ship is weel-rigged and ready to sail,
Our crew they are anxious to follow the whale,
Where the icebergs do float and the stormy
    winds blaw,
And the land and the ocean are covered wi'
    snaw.

3 The cold coast o' Greenland is barren and bare,
No seed-time nor harvest is ever known there,
And the birds here sing sweetly on mountain
    and dale,
But there isna a birdie tae sing tae the whale.

4 There is no habitation for a man to live there,
And the king of that country is the wild
    Greenland bear,
And there'll be no temptation to tarry long
    there,
With our ship bumper full we will homeward
    repair.

George Scroggie was miller at Federate in New Deer
Parish in 1850.
Many men left the land in the 19th and early
20th centuries to earn more money whaling.
Nowadays whales are an endangered species and the
men go to the oilrigs.

Central Lowlands

The craw killed the pussy-o

Words: JIMMIE MACGREGOR   Tune: TRADITIONAL

1 There was a wee bit mousiekie
That lived in Gilberatie-o,
He couldnae get a bite o' cheese
For cheetie pussy-catty-o.

2 Said mousie to the cheesikie
'Oh, fain wad I be at ye-o
If 'twere na for the cruel claws
O' cheetie pussy-catty-o

3 The craw killed the pussy-o
The craw killed the pussy-o,
The mammy cat sat doon and grat
In Johnny's wee bit hoosie-o.

4 We buried him on a Thursday-o
A thundery, thundery Thursday-o,
The midden men they said, 'Amen',
And I never saw a worse day-o.

5 Noo pussy's wi' the devil-o
Poor pussy's wi' the devil-o
And every moose in Johnny's hoose
Says, 'Gie that craw a medal-o'.

The first two verses are very old. The second part is usually a separate song with a traditional chorus and verses added by Jimmie Macgregor. I have combined them since they have the same tune and seem to make a story.

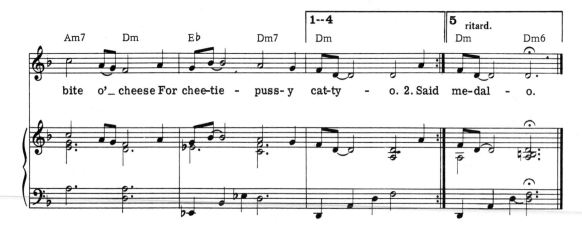

Willie Lee

1 Oh, I am a railway porter and my name is
    Willie Lee,
  You can search around the country frae
    Dumbarton tae Dundee,
  I'm the most important person that you're ever
    like tae see
  And my duty is tae tell ye whaur ye chinge fur . .
  YE CHINGE FUR . . .

  Auchterclochter, cuddlemadochter, Crieff or
    Callercoats,
  Land's End tae John o' Groats, Beecham's Pills
    or Quaker Oats.
  Ye chinge fur Ecclefechan, Aiberdeen an' a' the
    stations in between—
  Unless ye want tae gang tae Tobermory.

2 Oh, at Auchterclochter Junction if you're ever
    like tae be,
  Just pop your head frae the windae and you're
    sure tae notice me,
  I'm the most important person that you're ever
    like tae see
  And my duty is tae tell ye whaur ye chinge fur . . .
  YE CHINGE FUR . . .

  Auchterclochter, etc.

Continued overleaf

Willie Lee *(continued)*

3   Ae day at Auchterclochter Junction, oh I wis
       filled wi' pride!
   The royal train drew in and when I looked
       inside
   I saw Her Majesty, Lizzie, the Queen and the
       Duke wis by her side
   And they asked me a' the stations that ye chinge
       fur . . .
   AH TELT THEM . . .

Auchterclochter, cuddlemadochter, Crieff or
   Callercoats
Land's End tae John o' Groats, Beecham's Pills
   or Quaker Oats
Ye chinge fur Clachnacudden, Sands o' Budden
   and then ye buy a big mealy pudden—
Tae eat until ye gang tae Tobermory,
Tae eat until ye gang tae Tobermory.

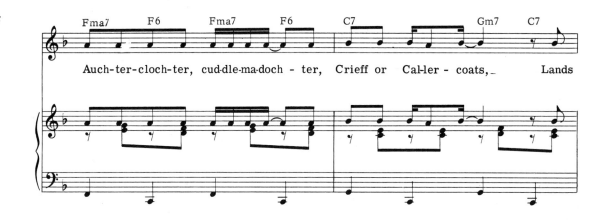

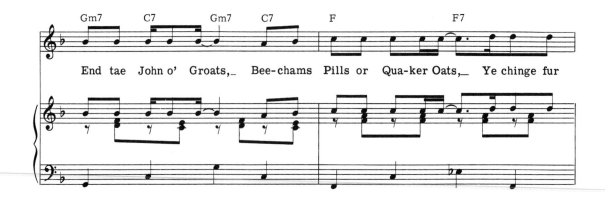

Ecc-le - fe-chan, Ai-ber-deen — an' a' the sta-tions in be - tween—Un-

less ye want tae gang tae To - ber-mo — ry. 2. Oh, at

mo - ry, Tae eat un-til ye gang tae To - ber-mo — ry.

Henry Martin

1 There were three brothers in merry Scotland
   In Scotland there lived brothers three,
   And they did cast lots which of them should
        go, should go, should go,
   For to turn robber all on the salt sea.

2 The lot it fell on Henry Martin
   The youngest of all the three,
   That he should turn robber all on the salt
        sea, the salt sea, the salt sea,
   For to maintain his two brothers and he.

3 He had not been sailing but a long winter's
        night
   And part of a short winter's day,
   When he espied a lofty stout ship, stout ship,
        stout ship,
   Coming a-sailing along that way.

4 'Hello, Hello,' said Henry Martin,
   'What makes you sail so high?'
   'I'm a rich merchant ship bound for fair
        London Town, London Town,
        London Town,
   Will you please for to let me pass by?'

5 'Oh no, Oh no!' cried Henry Martin,
   'That thing it never can be,
   For I have turned robber all on the salt sea,
        the salt sea, the salt sea,
   For to maintain my two brothers and me.'

72

6 With broadside and broadside and at it they
   went
   For fully two hours or three,
   Till Henry Martin gave to her the death
   shot, the death shot, the death shot,
   Heavily listing to starboard went she.

7 The rich merchant vessel was wounded full
   sore,
   Straight to the bottom went she,
   And Henry Martin sailed away on the sea,
   the salt sea, the salt sea,
   For to maintain his two brothers and he.

8 Bad news, bad news to old England came,
   Bad news to fair London Town,
   There was a rich vessel and she's cast away,
   cast away, cast away,
   And all of her merry men drowned.

*The pirate's real name was Andrew Barton. In 1476 a
Portuguese squadron seized a rich merchant ship
commanded by John Barton. The Scottish king,
James IV, gave letters of reprisal to his three sons,
Andrew, Robert and John. This was just royal
permission for piracy on the high seas.*

Andrew Barton went too far. His ship, the
Lion, *blockaded English ports and seized the cargoes
of English merchantmen pretending he thought
they were Portuguese.*

*Henry VIII sent his Lord High Admiral against
Andrew Barton. In the fight the* Lion *was captured
and Sir Andrew was fatally wounded.*

*A long ballad was written about him which has
suffered many sea-changes—not least to his name.*

The safari park song

JIMMIE MACGREGOR

We're going to the park in the country, hooray, hooray;
We're going to the park in the country, today, today.
We're going on safari, and we'll have a lovely day;
Hip hip hippopotamuses, hip hip hip hooray.

1 There's monkeys playing monkey games,
   Parrots calling people names;
   Hogs and hippopotamuses, fat from top to
      bottomuses.
   Lions lying in lazy lots,
   Leopards coming out in spots;
   Kangaroos and kinkajous,
   And owls with owly whit-tu-whoos.

   We're going, etc.

2 Donkey, deer and dromedary,
   Some are smooth and some are hairy;
   Some are gentle, some ferocious,
   Some are cute and some atrocious.
   Wart hogs in their warty hoggery,
   Dingoes in their dingo doggery;
   Beavers, bears and buffaloes,
   Flamingoes on their tippy toes.

   We're going, etc.

go-ing on Sa - fa - ri, and we'll have a love-ly day.

last time: **ritard.**   *FINE*

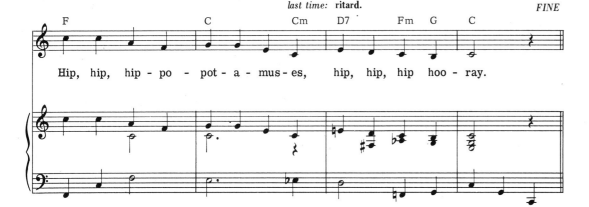

Hip, hip, hip - po - pot - a - mus - es, hip, hip, hip hoo - ray.

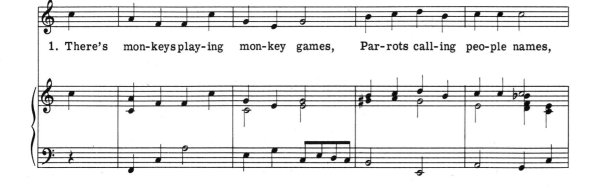

1. There's mon-keys play-ing mon-key games, Par-rots call-ing peo-ple names,

3   Take a peek at a pelican,
    Whose beak holds more than his belly can;
    Pythons, pigs and peccaries,
    Giraffes with stretchy neckaries.
    Dolphins in their dolphinariums,
    Fishes in their aquarariums.
    Racoon and rhinoceros,
    Looking quite prepoceros.

We're going, etc.

4   Crows and cranes and crocodiles,
    And children's faces wreathed in smiles;
    Camel rides for me and you,
    Do you prefer one hump or two?
    And when we're tired of having fun,
    A cup of tea and a sticky bun.
    Back in the car, and then away,
    To come again another day.

We're going, etc.

Two of the most popular Scottish safari parks are at Blair Drummond in Perthshire and Aviemore in Inverness-shire.

Continued overleaf

Bonnie George Campbell

1 High upon Hielands and laigh upon Tay,
Bonnie George Campbell rade oot on a day,
Saddled and bridled sae gallant and free,
Hame cam his guid horse but never cam' he.

2 Saddled and booted and bridled rade he
A plume at his helmet, a sword at his knee
But toom cam his saddle a' bluidy tae see,
Hame cam his guid horse but never cam' he.

3 Doon cam' his auld mither greetin' fu sair
Oot cam his bonnie wife rivin' her hair.
'My meadows lie green and my corn is unshorn.
My barn is tae bigg and my baby's unborn.'

4 High upon Hielands and laigh upon Tay,
Bonny George Campbell rade oot in a day,
Saddled and bridled sae gallant and free,
Hame cam his guid horse but never cam he.

George Campbell of Ardinglas had been appointed guardian to the young Earl of Argyll. Campbell of Calder was jealous and ordered his assassination. He was shot at night through a window at the House of Kneppoch in Lorne, pierced through the heart with three bullets supplied by Calder.

77

Jenny's bawbee

1 A that ere ma Jenny had
Ma Jenny had, ma Jenny had,
A' that ere ma Jenny had
Was a bawbee.
There's your plack and my plack,
There's your plack and my plack,
There's your plack and my plack,
And Jenny's bawbee.

2 D'ye ken na what ma granny did,
My granny did, my granny did?
D'ye ken na what ma granny did
For a bawbee?
She cockit up her widden leg,
Her widden leg, her widden leg,
She cockit up her widden leg
And blackit ma e'e.

The Lowlands of Scotland have their mouth music too. The next three songs are dance tunes. I have had children in my class practise their steps for the 'Sean Trews' to 'Jenny's Bawbee' because we had no suitable record to play.

The words are less important than the rhythm and the tune. Sometimes a singer will just diddle to the music to keep the dance going.

78

Katie Beardie

Tune: GABHAIDH SINN A RATHAD MOR

Not too fast

Ka-tie Bear-die had a coo, Black and white a-boot the mou', Was-nae that a dain-ty coo? Dance, Ka-tie Bear-die.

Ka-tie Bear-die had a hen, Cack-led but and cack-led ben.

Was-nae that a dain-ty hen? Dance, Ka-tie Bear-die. Bear-die.

1 Katie Beardie had a coo
Black and white aboot the mou'
Wasnae that a dainty coo?
Dance, Katie Beardie.

Katie Beardie had a hen,
Cackled but and cackled ben.
Wasnae that a dainty hen?
Dance, Katie Beardie.

2 Katie Beardie had a wean
Widnae play oot in the rain.
Wasnae that a dainty wean?
Dance, Katie Beardie.

Katie Beardie had a cat,
Sleek and sly and unco fat.
Wasnae that a dainty cat?
Dance, Katie Beardie.

Four and twenty Hielandmen

1 Four and twenty Hielandmen were riding on a
   snail,
   When up cam' the hindmost and trampit on her
   tail,
   Oh the snail shot out her wee horns just like a
   hummel coo,
   'Hech,' quo' the foremost, 'We'll a' be sticket
   noo!'

2 Four and twenty tailor lads were fightin wi' a'
   slug,
   'Hallo, sirs!' said ane o' them, 'Just haud him by
   the lug.'
   But the beastie frae his shell cam' oot and shook
   his fearsome head
   'Run, run, my tailors bold, or we will a' be
   dead!'

3 As I gaed by the mill door oot cam Miller Reid,
   His cap on his feet and his breeks upon his heid.
   An noo I've sung ye a' my song, I've telt it a',
   my friend,
   It's a' big lees frae beginning tae the end!

80

Edinburgh

The sack 'em up boys

JIMMIE MACGREGOR

Up the close and doon the stair,
But and ben wi' Burke and Hare;
Burke's the butcher. Hare's the thief.
Knox the boy who buys the beef.

1 Hurry doon the castle wynd,
   Look before and look behind;
   There they wait tae tak' yer life,
   And sell ye fur the surgeon's knife.

   Up the close, etc.

2 Auld or young or dark or fair,
   It makes nae mind tae Burke and Hare;
   While Dr Knox peys oot the tin,
   They'll sack'em up and bring 'em in.

   Up the close, etc.

3 Reekie's rows are dark and drear,
   Reekie's vennels reek wi' fear;
   Mind yersel' gaun doon the stair,
   Fur fear ye meet wi' Burke and Hare.

   Up the close, etc.

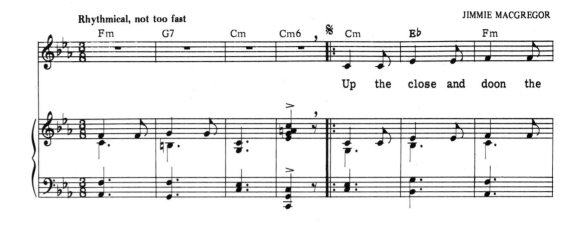

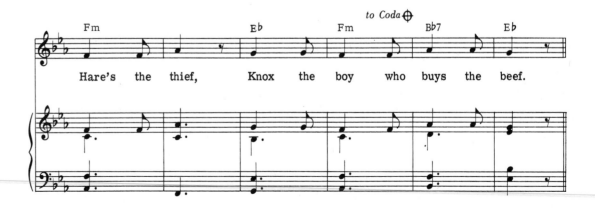

82

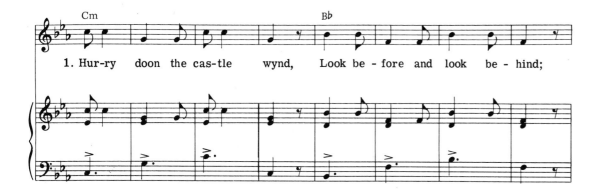

1. Hur-ry doon the cas-tle wynd, Look be-fore and look be-hind;

There they wait tae tak yer life, And sell ye fur the sur-geon's knife.

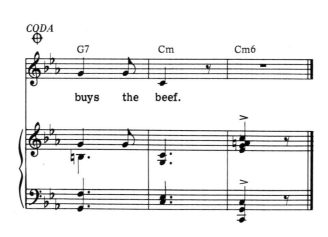

D.S. al Coda

Hare.

CODA

buys the beef.

Doctors need to study the anatomy of dead people to learn how to help the living. In the 19th century there was a thriving business selling corpses to medical schools. Graveyards had night watchmen and the graves of wealthy people were protected by iron cages called mortsafes.

William Burke came to Edinburgh from Ireland in 1818. He lived in William Hare's house where the lodgers were down-and-outs and drifters. When one died Burke and Hare sold the body to Dr Knox at the medical school for £7 10 shillings. They became greedy and began murdering people for their corpses, grew careless and were eventually caught.

Hare turned King's Evidence and was freed. Dr Knox had to leave Edinburgh in disgrace. William Burke was hanged on Jan 28th 1829. His body was dissected by the medical school and his skeleton is in Edinburgh University.

The chorus is an old street jingle. The verses are by Jimmie Macgregor.

The fair lady

1   As I went by the Luckenbooths I saw a lady fair,
    She had lang pendles in her ears and jewels in
        her hair
    And when she cam tae oor door she spiered at
        wha was ben,
    'Oh, hae ye seen my lost love wi' his braw
        Hieland men?'

2   The smile upon her bonny cheek was
        brighter than the bee,
    Her voice was like the birdie's sang upon the
        birken tree.
    But when the meenister cam' oot her mare
        began tae prance,
    And rode intae the sunset beyond the coast o'
        France.

*This is a children's ballad of the 17th century. The
Luckenbooths were market stalls in the High Street
in Edinburgh close to The High Kirk of St Giles.
They stood there from about 1470 until they were
demolished in 1817.*
    The lady was probably a ghost.

oor door she_ spiered at wha was ben, 'Oh,

hae ye seen my lost love wi'_ his braw Hie-land men?'

2. The_

Waly waly

1 O waly waly up the bank
And waly waly doon the brae,
And waly waly by yon burnside
Where I and my first love did gae.

2 I leaned my back against an oak
Thinkin' it was a trusty tree,
But first it bent and then it broke
And so did my first love tae me.

3 When we cam in frae Glasgow toun,
We were a comely sight tae see,
My love was clad in the velvet black
And I masel in cramasie.

4 Noo Arthur's Seat sall be my bed,
No sheets sall e'er be pressed by me,
Saint Anton's Well sall be my drink
Since my fause love's forsaken me.

5 'Tis not the frost that freezes fell
Nor blawin snaw's inclemency,
'Tis not sic cauld that makes me cry
But my love's heart's grawn cauld tae me.

6 Oh Martinmas wind when wilt thou blaw
And shake the green leaves off the tree?
Oh gentle death, when wilt thou come?
For of my life I am weary.

*Lord James Douglas rejected his wife because his
chamberlain told lies about her. This is her song.*

86

Riddles wisely expounded

1. A lady lived in the north countrie,
   Lay the bent tae the bonnie broom
   And she had lovely dochters three.
   Fal lal lal lal lal lal lal lal lal lah

2. There was a knight o' noble worth,
   Who also lived intae the north.

3. Ae nicht when it was cold and late,
   This knight he cam' tae the lady's gate.

4. The eldest dochter she let him in,
   She's pinned the door wi' a siller pin.

5. 'If you will answer me questions three,
   It's then, fair maid, I will marry thee.

6. Oh what is louder than a horn,
   And what is sharper than a thorn?

7. And what is longer than the way,
   And what is deeper than the sea?

8. And what is greener than the grass,
   And what more wicked than a woman ere
   was?'

9. 'Oh thunder's louder than a horn,
   And hunger's sharper than a thorn.

10. And love is longer than the way,
    And Hell is deeper than the sea.

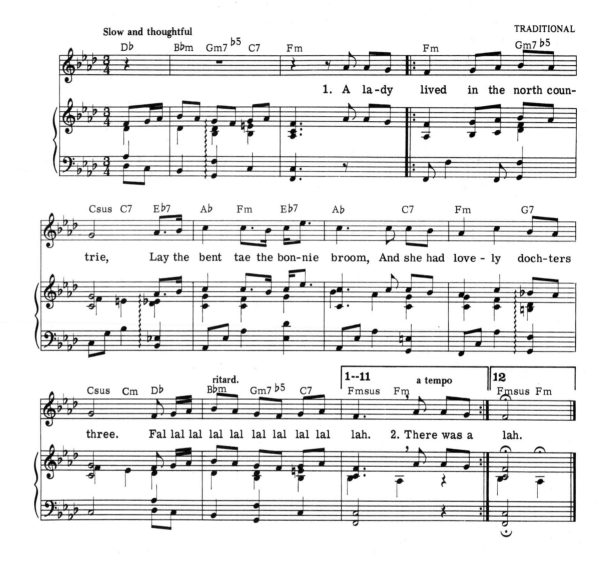

11. Envy's greener than the grass,
    And the Devil more wicked than a
    woman ere was.'

12. As soon as she the fiend did name,
    He flew awa' in a bleeze o' flame.

This song probably belongs to the North of England but the Border has moved to and fro across the Debatable Lands so often that I feel quite justified in calling it a Border ballad.

The italic lines repeat in each verse

The border widow's lament

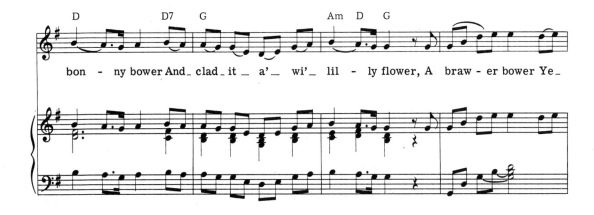

1 My love he built me a bonny bower
   And clad it a' wi' lily flower,
   A brawer bower ye ne'er did see
   Than my true love he built for me.

2 There came a man by middle day
   He spied his sport and went away,
   And brought the king that very night
   Who brak' my bower and slew my knight.

3 He slew my knight to me sae dear
   He slew my knight and poined his gear.
   The servants all for life did flee
   And left me in extremity.

4 I took his body on my back
   And whiles I gaed and whiles I sat,
   I digged a grave and laid him in
   And happed him wi' the sod sae green

5 Nae living man I'll love again
   Since that my lovely knight was slain
   Wi' ae lock o' his gowden hair
   I'll chain my heart for evermair.

Sir Walter Scott claimed that this ballad was heard in the Forest of Ettrick. It concerned Cockburn of Henderland, a border reiver who was hanged over the gate of his own tower by James V in 1529.

The ruins of Henderland are by the Meggat Burn and the spot where Lady Cockburn fled during her husband's execution is still called The Lady's Seat.

Lock the door, Lariston

JAMES HOGG

1 Lock the door, Lariston, lion of Liddesdale,
Lock the door, Lariston, Lowther comes on.
The Armstrongs are flying, the widows are
      crying,
Castletown is burning and Oliver is gone!
Lock the door, Lariston, high on the weather
      gleam,
See how the Saxon plumes they bob on the sky.
Yeoman and carbinier, billman and halberdier,
Fierce is the foray and far is the cry!

2 Why d'you smile, noble Elliot o' Lariston?
Why do the joy candles gleam in your eye?
You bold Border ranger, beware of your danger,
Your foes are relentless, determined and nigh!
'I have Mangerton and Ogilvie, Raeburn and
      Netherbie,
Auld Sim o' Whitram and all his array,
Come all Northumberland, Teesdale and
      Cumberland
Here at the Breaken Tower end shall the fray'.

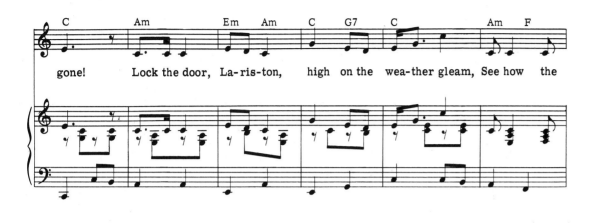

gone! Lock the door, La-ris-ton, high on the wea-ther gleam, See how the
Sax-on plumes they bob on the sky.

Yeo - man and car-bin-ier, bill - man and
hal-ber-dier, Fierce is the for-ay and far is the cry! aye!

3 Scowled the broad sun o'er the links o' green
        Liddesdale,
   Red as the beacon-fires tipped he the wold,
   Many a bold martial eye mirrored that morning
        sky,
   Never more oped on its orbit of gold.
   See how they wane the proud files o' the
        Windermere.
   Howard! Ah woe tae your hopes o' the day.
   Hear the wide welkin rend while the Scots
        shouts ascend—
   'Elliot o' Lariston! Elliot for aye!'

Border reiving, stealing and plundering from one's neighbour, was a recognized way of life. All the farms were fortified keeps. The cattle were protected by swords. The songs of this region are the great ballads, long, grim and heavy. There was no time for humour.

Glossary

aboot *about*
abune *above*
afore *before*
agin *against*
ain *own*
Arthur's Seat *volcanic hill in Edinburgh*
atween *between*
a' the lave *everyone else*
auld *old*
Auld Reekie *Edinburgh*

baillie loon *cowman*
bairns *children*
barra *barrow*
Barras *Glasgow street market*
barley-bree *whisky*
bash *a turn, a ride*
bawbee *old halfpenny*
begat *fathered*
ben *into the living-room*
bide a wee *wait a while*
bigg, biggit *build, built*
birken *birch*
birl *spin*
blate *shy*
blear *redden the eyes*
bogie *homemade boxcart*
bool *marble*
brae *hillside*
braw *fine, handsome*
breist-straps *harness*
breeks *trousers*
breid *bread*
brochan *porridge*
brochan lom *thin porridge*
Broomielaw *a dockside street in Glasgow*

but and ben *back and fore, in and out*
byre *cowshed*

callants *youths*
chappin' *knocking*
chittering *shivering*
claespole *prop for a washing-line*
clachan *hamlet*
cloods *clouds*
clorts *clarts, spreads*
close *tunnel-like entrance to a tenement*
cockit *lifted*
comeallye *folksong*
cooper *a man who makes barrels*
couldny *couldn't*
craw *crow*
croon *crown, head, top of a hat*
crousely *boldly*
cuddie's jaw *the jawbone of an ass*

da *the*
dat, daet *that*
daud *lump*
dee *thee, you*
deen *done*
dere *there*
dings *knocks down*
doon *down*
drift *snowdrift*
du *thou, you*
dy *your*

e'e *eye*
e'en *evening, eyes*

een *one*
exciseman *Customs officer*
eynoo *just now*

factor *bailiff*
fan *when*
fankle *tangle*
fee *wealth*
fee'd *apprenticed*
fell *grim, ghastly*
fir *for*
fitba' *football*
flair *floor*
forbye *besides*
furt *out of doors*

gaed on *was promoted*
gaffer *foreman*
gallus *bold, confident*
gang *go*
gansey *guernsey pullover*
gar *make*
gaun *going*
geans *wild cherry*
geng *go*
gied *gave*
gird and cleek *hoop and stick*
girn *make faces, complain*
gowd *gold*
gowk *cuckoo, idiot*
grat *wept*
greeting *crying*
guid *good*

happed *wrapped*
haud *hold*
heelster-gowdie *head over heels*
heugh *crag, pit, hollow*

heid *head*
hoodies *crows*
hoose *house*
hummel coo *horned cow*
hurl *ride*

ida *in the*
ilka *every*
intae *into*

jannie *janitor, school caretaker*
jaurie *glass marble*
jist *just*
jyle *gaol, prison*

ken *know*
keek *a look*
kirkie *church*
kitchie-deen *woman who works in a farm kitchen*
knappin' knees *knock knees*
kye *cattle, cows*
kyin *ken, know*

laigh *low*
lang *long*
lave *the others, leave*
leck *leak*
lees *lies*
lirkit up *moved up in creases*
loanings *lodgings*
lug *ear*
lum hat *top hat*

Mahoun' *Mahomet, Auld Nick, the Devil*
mair *more*
makes nae mind *doesn't matter*

malt *liquor, whisky*

maun *must*

mealy pudden *a spicy oatmeal sausage*

midden *rubbish tip*

mither *mother*

mony *tomorrow*

mouter *fee for grinding corn*

muckle *many big much*

nippit *nipped frozen*

oot *out*

ower *over*

partan *crab*

peady *little*

peerie *spinning-top*

pendles *earrings*

piece *sandwich*

pibroch *classical pipe music*

plack *halfpence*

plaidie *plaid shawl*

ploys *games*

plunk *to shoot a marble*

poined *confiscated*

polisman *policeman*

pooch *pocket*

puir *poor*

quo' *quoth, said*

reekie *smoky, smelly*

rend *tear*

rickle o' banes *skeleton*

riggit *roofed*

riving *tearing*

roch *rough*

rock *distaff*

rottans *rats*

sairly *sorely*

sall *shall*

sanna *shall not*

saugh *sloe*

shoon *shoes*

sic *such*

siller *silver*

single-end *one-roomed tenement flat*

siver *sewer, a drain*

skyting *flying off at speed in a slanting direction*

slogans *warcries*

sneck *latch*

sookin' *sucking*

soomin' *swimming*

spate *flood*

spiered *asked*

spinnel trams *spindly legs*

stane-blin' *stone-blind, totally blind*

sticket *stuck*

strathspeys *dances*

sweer *unwilling*

syne *since*

taatit-rug *rug made of woollen threads*

tapsalteerie *upside down*

telt *told*

thegither *together*

thrifty *piggy-bank*

toom *empty*

trowie *miserable*

twae *two*

unco *strange*

vennel *alley*

verra *very*

waukin' *waking*

wean *child*

welt *blow*

wellies *wellington boots*

whaur *where*

whit *what*

widden *wooden*

widnae *wouldn't*

wisnae *wasn't*

wynd *lane or narrow alley in a town*

yont *beyond*

Acknowledgements

Our thanks to the Scottish Tourist Board for supplying and allowing us to use the photographs in this book.

Cover: Pennan, Aberdeenshire
Highlands and Islands: Sligachan
Galloway: Glen Trool
Grampian: Gardenstown, Banff
Edinburgh: Scott Monument and Castle

Title page: Loch Linnhe
Glasgow: George Square
Orkney and Shetland: Ring of Brogar
Central Lowlands: Aberfeldy
Borders: Eildon Hills

We should also like to thank the following for permission to reproduce copyright material:

The Sir Hugh Roberton Trust and Roberton Publications for the words of *Air falalalo;*
Westminster Music Ltd, 19/20 Poland Street, London W9V 3DD, for *The Dark Island;*
John McGrath for the words of *The Battle of the Braes;*
EMI Music Publishing Ltd and International Music Publications for *The welly boot song* (© 1974 EMI Music Publishing Ltd) and for the words of *Faraway Tom* (© 1969 Robbins Music Corporation Ltd, London);
Harmony Music Ltd, 19/20 Poland St, London W9V 3DD for the words and music of *The red yo-yo;*
James S Kerr, 65 Berkeley Street, Glasgow G3 for *The song of the Clyde;*
The executors of Matt McGinn's estate for *The wee Kirkcudbright centipede;*
Mrs Martha Robertson for her late husband's words to *Da rabbit's lullaby* and Larry Peterson for the music;
The School of Scottish Studies for *Willie Lee* (collected by Hamish Henderson);
Jimmie Macgregor for the words and music of *The safari park song* and *The sack 'em up boys* and for additional words to *O'Hara's barra, The craw killed the pussy-o* and *Sound the Pibroch.*

We have made every effort to trace the owners of copyright material but in some cases this has not been possible. We apologise for any omissions and should be glad to be notified of them.

Music books from Ward Lock Educational

Song books

The Funny Family   Alison McMorland
An entertaining selection of singing games, nursery rhymes and folk songs, which will be enjoyed and treasured by young and old alike. Simple guitar chords and melody lines or piano accompaniment are provided, and children will enjoy the humorous illustrations.   **ISBN 0 7062 3719 6**

Brown Bread and Butter   Alison McMorland
A further selection of songs, singing games and rhymes for every occasion. Many fine old favourites and captivating new discoveries have been brought together to be enjoyed wherever children play, and wherever strong local traditions still exist.   **ISBN 0 7062 4196 7**

Knock at the Door   Jan Betts
A comprehensive collection of songs, poems and rhymes which are popular today with young children. Very simple guitar chords and melody lines are provided, and the delightful illustrations will provide many hours of enjoyment for children.   **ISBN 0 7062 4029 4**

Folk Carols for Young Children   Barbara Cass-Beggs
A bright, international selection of carols and nursery rhymes, which includes many traditional Christmas carols as well as some for other festivals from several countries. A brief note on the origin of each carol and suggestions for accompanying dance movements are included.   **ISBN 0 7062 4046 4**

A Musical Calendar of Festivals   Barbara Cass-Beggs
A collection of songs from all over the world, grouped into months with clear explanations of their appropriateness to particular festivals. The songs are beautifully illustrated and have both melody and guitar chording for accompaniment.   **ISBN 0 7062 42262**

Barnabas the Dancing Bear   Diana Holland
These five plays, based on both original and well-known stories, will be greatly enjoyed by 5–8 year olds. Each play combines catchy songs with short speaking parts and offers scope for percussion work, dancing, choruses etc. All the plays are attractively illustrated.   **ISBN 0 7062 4225 4**

Sing as You Grow   Brenda I. Piper
The original songs in this delightful collection have been written for the very young, and are designed to encourage physical, mental, emotional and social skills. Guitar chords are included, together with suggestions for untuned percussion. Understanding and enjoyment is enhanced by the clear, bright illustrations.   **ISBN 0 7062 4158 4**

Every Colour Under the Sun
Songs on thoughtful themes for primary school assemblies

The songs in this exciting collection (many of them original) are grouped into themes: the seasons, the world around us, faith and prayer, work and everyday duties, helping others, working towards a better world, celebrations, beginnings and endings etc. Here is the answer to the teacher's need for musical material to span the range of cultures and faiths found in many schools today.**ISBN 0 7062 4266**

Jump into the Ring   Lesley Lees
A whole new treasury of original action songs and rhymes for young children. Simple piano accompaniments and guitar chords are provided plus helpful ideas for organisation and presentation. The songs, rhymes and tunes all have a strong rhythmic content, inviting and encouraging movement.
ISBN 0 7062 4294 7

Silly Aunt Sally   Jan Holdstock
Share a joke with your class with this illustrated collection of original songs which appeal to children's love of the ridiculous. Some of the songs have accompanying actions or games and all of them have fresh, catchy tunes pitched at the right level for young voices. Full piano accompaniments, guitar chords and suggestions for percussion work.

Alphabet Zoo Songbook   Ralph McTell
Here are all the favourite songs from Ralph McTell's children's television programmes—arranged for the piano for the first time. They range from the lyrical to the delightfully absurd and make the ideal basis for a school entertainment (performance suggestions are provided). Chris Masters' illustrations catch the mood of the songs perfectly. Factual details about some of the more unusual animals, illustrated with finely-detailed engravings, complete the book.   **ISBN 0 7062 4423 0**

Assemblies Round the Year   Beverley Birch
This collection of assembly readings for primary schools also includes the words and music for 14 assembly songs which reflect the highlights of the school year.
ISBN 07062 4469 9

Other music books

Musical Starting Points with Young Children   Jean Gilbert
This book outlines a number of starting points in musical activities that can help the class teacher with no specialist music training to integrate the subject into the daily timetable. The singing games, finger plays and songs in the book encourage movement and dance and, ultimately, physical and emotional development.   **ISBN 0 7062 4045 6**